C000184406

a gif

to: **mummy** ....

from: **maisie** ....

OTHER HELEN EXLEY GIFTBOOKS IN THIS SERIES:
Me and my Dad
Me and my Grandma
Me and my Grandad

OTHER HELEN EXLEY GIFTBOOKS:
Forever my Mum
To a very special Mother
To a lovely Mother

To Pam, All My Love, Jane x
To Marion, my mom. Just to say that every word in this book is true.
With all my love, Helen x

First published in 2005 by Helen Exley Giftbooks in
Great Britain, and Helen Exley Giftbooks LLC in the USA.
This edition published in 2010.

12 11 10 9 8 7 6 5 4 3 2 1

Illustrations © Jane Massey 2005, 2010
Copyright © Helen Exley 2005, 2010
The moral right of the author has been asserted.

ISBN 978-1-84634-522-7

Helen Exley Giftbooks,
16 Chalk Hill, Watford,
Herts WD19 4BG, UK.
www.helenexleygiftbooks.com

Me
and my
Mum

Written by Helen Exley and Illustrated by Jane Massey

This is my Mum.

She is really fun.

She sings and dances with me.

Jumping, thumping, laughing...

we make a lot of noise.

My Mum's hands
are really kind and gentle.
When I hurt my arm
she mended me and teddy too.
She looks after
everyone.

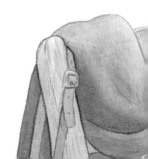

My Mum has to work so that we can buy things. I don't know how she doesn't get driven mad by the computer, the homework the phone, ME!

She really loves me, you know.

Sometimes my Mum is naughty.

when we go shopping she says
"My feet are killing me!"
So we take off our shoes
and put our feet in the fountain.
"Ahh," she says, "that's better."

One day my Mum was very tired.

She said, "I've had quite enough!"

So I tucked her in

and gave her

some peace and quiet.

My Mum protects me.

she helps me not to fall off my bike (and do other dangerous, silly things!). She would stop anyone else from hurting me. She is very brave and makes me brave too.

My Mum is always busy -

she has too much to do.

washing, rushing, cooking,

tidying my toys. It never stops.

Poor Mum!

I give my Mum lessons.
She is really useless
because she can't Kick and she
can't catch.

I tell her, "Keep trying Mum,

I love you anyway."

My Mum is a softie.

when we sit on the sofa

and watch her old movies

she cries. we cry together.

My Mum is kind. We work together on my reading and my sums. If I really, really try she gives me a star, even when I get them wrong!

One night I had a bad dream.

The scary crocodiles and lions were coming to get me. Mum hugged me and read me to sleep. When she is there I always feel safe.

My Mum has special times for me

No matter how busy she is, we do

our own thing. Just me and my

Mum. Reading, dancing, laughing

going off together...

This is my really special Mum.

WHAT IS A HELEN EXLEY GIFTBOOK?

Helen Exley Giftbooks cover the most powerful
of all human relationships: the bonds within
families and between friends,
and the theme of personal values.
No expense is spared in making sure that
each book is as meaningful
a gift as it is possible to create: good to give,
good to receive.
You have the result in your hands.
If you have loved it –
tell others! There is no power on earth
like the word-of-mouth
recommendation of friends!